C000227319

A PARRAGON BOOK

Published by Parragon Book Service Ltd,
Units 13-17, Avonbridge Trading Estate, Atlantic Road,
Avonmouth, Bristol BS11 9QD

Produced by The Templar Company plc,
Pippbrook Mill, London Road, Dorking,
Surrey RH4 1JE

Written by Peter Gray
Edited by Caroline Ball
Illustrations by Peter Bull Art Studio

Printed and bound in the UK

ISBN 0 7525 1697 3

FACTFINDERS

HANDGUNS & SMALL ARMS

‖ ·PARRAGON· ‖

CONTENTS

INTRODUCTION

This book aims to give an insight into the evolution of small arms through history. It cannnot, of course, be an in-depth study of all firearms, but concentrates on those guns which have come to be seen as landmarks in the development of small arms and with those handguns, rifles, sub-machine-guns and general-purpose machine-guns that are generally accepted as being of particular interest.

The story of the gun begins with the invention of gunpowder, for without this fast-burning mixture giving off great quantities of expanding gases there would have been no cannon or hand gonne. Experimentation with methods of igniting this powerful propellant led to the development of the matchlock, flintlock and, in due course, the change from muzzle to breechloading. This latter development caught on thanks to the invention of the percussion cap, made possible by Alexander Forsyth's detonating powder (see Percussion System, page 20). It is interesting to consider how the history books would have been rewritten had Forsyth taken up Napoleon's offer to acquire his lock mechanism.

Sadly, it has usually been the demands of warfare that have been at the root of advances in firearms. Not without reason was gunpowder known as black powder. Soldiers had to deal with the frequent fouling up of their weapon's bores by sooty deposits. Gunpowder created a lot of smoke and also gave low muzzle velocities. Smokeless powder not only resulted in very slight fouling, but also produced very little smoke, enabling hidden marksmen to operate successfully for the first time. The higher pressures of smokeless powder also opened the way for smaller, lighter bullets, higher velocities and greater range. A musket might, with luck, hit a man at 70m (76 yd); a modern rifle with telescopic sights brings a target 2000m (2200 yd) away within range.

Guns hold a certain fascination for many people. This interest can either come from an active sport where guns are used, past experiences with them or simply a wish to own or shoot a particular weapon. The majority of the weapons illustrated were developed for military purposes, but thousands of people take part in recreational shooting, from clay pigeon or competition target shooting to game hunting or firing original and reproduction muzzleloaders. Whatever the interest, guns should always be treated with respect, handled and stored responsibly and never placed in a position to cause harm to another person.

It is hoped that this pocket-sized book will engage the interest and whet the appetites of those who wish to learn more of the absorbing history of small arms.

HAND GONNE

The origin of gunpowder is not certain. Records show that the Chinese had fireworks perhaps as early as the ninth century. Whoever the inventor was, his discovery would change the mode of warfare and influence the course of history. The first known military use of gunpowder has been dated to the thirteenth century and it remained the only explosive used in warfare for 600 years.

The earliest record of a gun appears in a manuscript of 1326 and shows a pear-shaped cannon firing an arrow. By the 1350s references to the first 'hand gonnes' began to appear. The barrels of these early guns were generally cast in bronze or iron with a bore of up to 4cm (1.5 in). In some cases the barrel was cast with both ends open and would be sealed with an iron plug before it was

fixed to a wooden staff with iron bands. This crude, heavy device was innacurate and less effective than a longbow or crossbow but it gave great psychological advantages to the armies that employed it.

The gun was loaded down the muzzle with a charge of gunpowder, wadding and the projectile, which might be an iron ball, a large stone or smaller shot. The touch hole at the breach end was filled with powder and ignited with an iron rod heated in a fire. Later a slow match consisting of hemp soaked in saltpetre was used instead. This revolutionary change would lead to the invention of the matchlock.

Few examples of hand gonnes exist. Perhaps the best known is one found in a well at Tannenburg Castle, which was razed to the ground in 1399. A bronze hand gonne in excellent condition has also been unearthed in Sweden.

The hand gonne, a crude device for firing a projectile using gunpowder as the propellant. The short iron or bronze barrel is shown fixed to the longer wooden staff with iron bands.

The slow match, once ignited, could be carried for several hours and was clearly a more convenient way of igniting gunpowder than the heated iron rod.

There were some disadvantages, however. The gunner needed to hold on to the slow match and apply it to the touch hole, which meant taking his eyes off the target. The answer came in the early part of the 15th century. Records of this time show a hand gonne with a Z-shaped arm holding a slow match. The arm is pivoted on the wooden staff and by moving one end the gunner brings the end holding the match down to the touch hole.

The system was refined by incorporating a small pan for priming powder on the side of the breach and doing away with the touch hole on top. The pan had a sliding or pivoting cover to protect the powder from the elements or stray sparks. Further refinements saw the addition of a spring-loaded arm that snapped down on to the priming powder – the snapping matchlock.

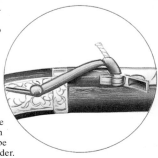

By this time the wooden staff had become the stock, along the lines of the modern stock, which enabled the gun to be fired from the shoulder. Some very heavy guns were usually supported on a forked rest. The heavier guns were called arquebuses and the lighter ones muskets.

The matchlock musket showing the more usual shape for the stock and the Z-shaped arm or 'serpentine' holding the smouldering match. The inset shows in more detail the open pan cover. In use in Europe from the early 15th until the 17th century, they were still used in Japan, China and India until modern times.

WHEEL-LOCK

The matchlock had two main disadvantages. It could not be used in damp weather, and the glowing matches gave away the gunners' positions at night. However, it was cheap to manufacture and remained the principal military firearm for around 200 years.

Firearms were also being used for sporting purposes and it was in this field that the next major development took place. Some have attributed the invention of the wheel-lock to Leonardo da Vinci but it is more likely that Johan Kuhfuss, or Kiefuss, a clockmaker of Nuremberg was the inventor, some time prior to 1510.

Like the matchlock, the wheel-lock was loaded from the muzzle, but here the similarity ends. In the wheel-lock a piece of iron pyrites was held firmly against a serrated

An ornate German wheel-lock carbine.

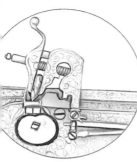

The iron pyrites held against the spinning serrated wheel.

to fly from the iron pyrites, which would ignite the waiting priming powder.

More complex mechanisms evolved, culminating in a lock that caused the arm holding the stone to snap into the pan, the pan cover to open and the wheel to revolve. This type of ignition allowed the weapon to be carried concealed. The first pistols of this type appeared around 1518. Ignition was fast and effective but the

wheel that protruded into the priming pan. The wheel was then wound up like a clock and when released by pulling the trigger it would revolve very fast, causing sparks

expense of manufacture resulted in the wheel-lock being used by private owners for sport rather than the military; consequently some extremely elaborate examples exist.

FLINTLOCK

The principle of making sparks to ignite the priming powder was firmly established with the wheel-lock. What was now needed was a version that could be easily and cheaply made.

The answer was the snaphaunce. This had a 'cock', a spring-loaded arm which was cocked back prior to firing. When the trigger was pulled the spring was released and the cock flew forward to strike a pivoted steel held above the

priming pan. At the same time the pan cover automatically moved forward allowing sparks to fall into the pan.

Some believe the snaphaunce originated in Holland, but others consider it a German invention. In any case it was in use throughout

The pistol shown is a typical high-quality Italian snaphaunce.

most of northern Europe around the beginning of the 17th century.

In Spain there evolved the miquelet lock, in which the steel and the pan cover were joined together. The cock carrying the flint hit the steel, or frizzen, which was held in place by an external spring. The frizzen pivoted when struck, enabling the sparks to fall into the pan.

The flint about to strike the steel to cause sparks.

The true or French flint-lock evolved from these two earlier systems, the real improvement being a better method of holding and releasing the cock.

The flintlock system proved to be efficient and comparatively cheap to produce, and it became a widely used standard military weapon.

THE PERCUSSION SYSTEM

The flintlock was faster than its predecessors, but there was still a delay between pulling the trigger and the ignition of the charge in the breech. On firing you can hear the 'phew' of the primer burning prior to the explosion of the main charge. It was also open to the elements.

The solution came from Alexander Forsyth, a

Scottish minister who was a keen shot and amateur chemist. Edward Howard had discovered fulminate of mercury, which would detonate when struck, and in 1807 Forsyth patented a system that used a detonating powder based on potassium chloride.

The pistol shown is a military holster pistol with swivel ramrod.

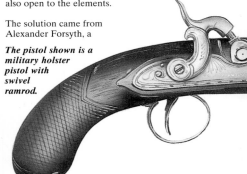

In early attempts, the powder container itself exploded, but he finally perfected the 'scent bottle' lock, a small magazine that pivoted around the vent to deposit a measure of detonating powder. When triggered, the hammer struck a firing pin, detonating the powder and igniting the charge.

Attempts to simplify the method of containing the powder led to the invention, around 1820, of the percussion cap. This small copper cap of detonating powder was placed on a nipple that formed part of the breech. When struck by the hammer the small explosion that resulted travelled through the nipple to ignite the charge. This single invention would lead the way to the modern cartridge and the breechloader.

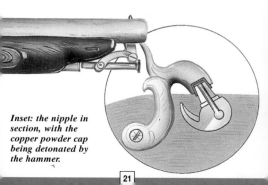

Inset: the nipple in section, with the copper powder cap being detonated by the hammer.

BREECHLOADER

There had been breech-loaders since the early days of cannon, but until the percussion method was perfected the muzzle loader predominated. The breechloader saw much

A common Belgian 9mm pinfire six-shot double-action revolver, c. 1860.

success during the 1860s. Various designs involved sliding, pivoting and bolt-sealing systems but the principle behind them all was virtually the same. A cartridge (a projectile attached to its propellant,

The hammer, having driven the pin into the cartridge case to ignite the detonating powder.

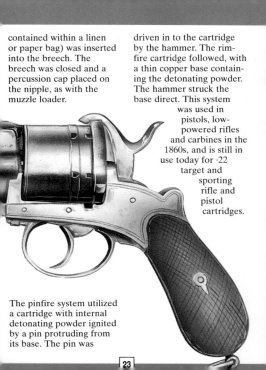

contained within a linen or paper bag) was inserted into the breech. The breech was closed and a percussion cap placed on the nipple, as with the muzzle loader.

driven in to the cartridge by the hammer. The rimfire cartridge followed, with a thin copper base containing the detonating powder. The hammer struck the base direct. This system was used in pistols, lowpowered rifles and carbines in the 1860s, and is still in use today for ·22 target and sporting rifle and pistol cartridges.

The pinfire system utilized a cartridge with internal detonating powder ignited by a pin protruding from its base. The pin was

CENTRE-FIRE CARTRIDGE

In the late 1850s Clement Pottet in Paris was the first to make a shotgun cartridge with a metal base having a percussion cap in the centre. The British Army were looking for a way of converting the muzzle-loading ·577 Enfield rifle to breechloading. The American Jacob Snider provided the answer. His rifle (see page 36) used a centre-fire cartridge similar to Pottet's. It had a brass base and, initially, a card case, which did not completely seal the rifle breech.

Colonel Edward Boxer invented a coiled brass case for the Snider cartridge, which did seal the breech effectively. This success led to a further improvement in

the drawn brass cartridge, which was possibly first

produced by Paul Mauser of Germany around 1869. For the first time the cartridge was completely rigid, unlike its predecessors, which were rather fragile. This opened the door for weapons that fed the cartridges into the breech automatically. The era of self-loading and fully automatic weapons was about to commence.

The pistol illustrated here is a 9mm Beretta, adopted

by the US armed forces several years ago. It is a locked breech self-loader and relies on the force of the exploding cartridge to move the barrel and

The 9mm Beretta self-loading pistol: a double-action system with a high-capacity 15-round magazine in the butt.

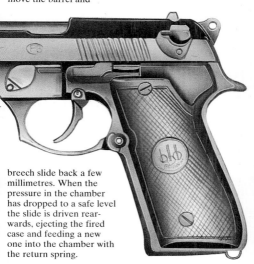

breech slide back a few millimetres. When the pressure in the chamber has dropped to a safe level the slide is driven rearwards, ejecting the fired case and feeding a new one into the chamber with the return spring.

BROWN BESS MUSKET

This was the flintlock muzzle-loading musket carried by the British army in various forms from around 1730 to the late 1830s. No one is sure of the origin of the name – it may have been from the colour of the stock or perhaps the barrel.

The first pattern was known as the Long Land musket and had a 1.17m (46in) barrel with a 2cm (0.75in) bore and weighed 4kg (10lb). It used a wooden ramrod. In 1740 it was replaced by the slightly shorter Short Land musket which was in all other respects very similar to the longer weapon. Wooden ramrods were soon replaced by iron ones.

Towards the latter part of the 18th century a cheaper musket was adopted, but in the 1800s the better made New Land Pattern

The Short Land musket with 106cm (42in) barrel and 2cm (0.75in) bore had brass trigger guard and ramrod pipes and an iron ramrod. It was the principal infantry weapon of the Colonial and Napoleonic wars. In 1741 the price of a Brown Bess was equivalent to about 80p.

was issued. All these muskets had approximately the same bore and differed mainly in barrel length and weight. They were all designed to carry a 43cm (17in) bayonet.

Loaded with powder from a paper cartridge and a loose-fitting ball, the musket was not an accurate weapon. However, infantry warfare at the time was conducted by massed ranks advancing and firing at their opposite numbers from a range of only about 50m (54yd), and then charging with fixed bayonets.

When the need for light infantry became apparent, shorter carbines similar to those carried by cavalry and artillery men were issued. These shorter and lighter weapons were of smaller bore and in the hands of skirmishers led the way to the use of the rifle in battle. The musket had the advantage of a faster rate of fire – trained troops could fire three rounds per minute.

BLUNDERBUSS

The blunderbuss was principally a flintlock weapon, having a 30–46cm (12–18in) barrel and a 2.5–4cm (1–1.5in) bore with a flared muzzle. The name probably derives from the German *donder* (thunder) and *bus* (gun). It was thought that the bell-mouthed muzzle assisted in spreading the shot, which could consist of anything from birdshot to buckshot or a number of pistol balls. In fact the muzzle shape made little difference, although it did have a tremendous psychological effect on anyone facing it. It was also of great benefit to anyone attempting to load the gun on a moving stage coach.

The gun was primarily used by coach guards against highwaymen and by private citizens to protect their homes. Some models included a bayonet attachment.

used by the Navy for the same purpose. The volley gun was a ·46 bore, seven-barrelled flintlock weapon that discharged all seven barrels at once.

Blunderbuss were also produced in the form of pistols and, although they were never as popular as the shoulder arm, these smaller weapons were often ornately decorated.

Although not a military weapon, the blunderbuss was sometimes used by the Royal Navy for deck clearing. It should not be confused, however, with the volley gun, a heavy, fearsome weapon that was

A typical flintlock blunderbuss pistol, with brass barrel and folding bayonet. This was spring-loaded and released by pulling back the trigger guard.

BAKER RIFLE

Up to now we have not considered the differences between the smoothbore and the rifle. The smoothbore musket was fired at close range. With the issue loose-fitting ball you would be lucky to hit a man-sized target above 70m (76yd). A rifled barrel, with grooves cut to give a twist to a tight-fitting bullet increased accuracy to two or three times that of the smoothbore, even in the early versions.

Towards the end of the 18th century volunteer corps were being formed and many were foreigners who were conversant with the continental hunting rifle. This seemed to be one reason for the ordnance to look for a rifle for use by the military. In 1800 Colonel Coote Manningham was instructed to command a corps of special riflemen. Formed from fourteen line regiments the Rifle Corps became the 95th and later the Rifle Brigade. A trial at Woolwich took place in February 1800 to decide which rifle would be selected and one produced by Ezekiel Baker was chosen. Baker's rifle was a flintlock with a 75cm (30in) barrel. Its bore had seven grooves and a twist of one quarter turn in its length. Its weight varied between 3.8 and 4kg (8.5–9lb). It was generally ·65 calibre, although early ones were ·70. Early models had a large butt box to carry the patches and tools issued with the rifle. The smaller butt box on later models carried only patches and spare flints. All models had front and rear sights.

The success of the Baker's 'accuracy' relied upon the use of a patched ball that had to be rammed down the barrel. The thickness of the patch corresponded to the depth of the grooves which formed the rifling. Powder charges were accurately dispensed from paper cartridges or from a powder horn. Baker's demonstration target, about 1810, shows 24 shots at 180m (200yd) within an area about 45cm wide by 90cm high (18 by 36in), the majority of shots hitting a man-sized target. This weapon was still in use in 1836.

The flintlock Baker rifle was carried by the Rifle Brigade up to the late 1830s. It was used in action at El Ferrol in north-west Spain in 1800 and played a major part in defeating Napoleon at Waterloo.

·577 ENFIELD

During the flintlock era the projectile was a ball patched with linen or leather to grip the rifling in the barrel, giving accuracy up to about 200m (217yd) (see page 31) but after a few shots the grooves became fouled by the powder, making it virtually impossible to load and inaccurate when fired. Various methods were devised whereby a loose-fitting ball could be dropped down the barrel and then expanded in the breech. It was reasoned that the bullet, being slightly larger than the bore, would then take the rifling and spin.

The answer came from M. Delvigne of France around 1840. He discovered that a long cylindrical bullet with a hollow base could be expanded to fit the grooves. Capitaine Minié carried out experiments with an iron cup in the hollow base of the bullet from which the ·702 Minié rifle evolved. This was the forerunner of the Enfield ·577 rifle. The principle that a lead projectile whose length is twice its diameter will expand under the force of the explosion was set. Twenty-five bore (·577) was selected and the Pritcher bullet adopted which could be easily loaded down a fouled bore and yet expand to fill the grooves. The rifleman now had a really efficient weapon which was accurate and easy to load.

There were several models, differing in barrel length, number of grooves and from brass to iron furniture. The P53, which had a 1m (39in) barrel, was for general infantry, while sergeants and the Rifle Brigade were issued with the shorter 83cm (33in) P56. There were others for naval and artillery use, but all fired the same bullet with varying powder charges in the cartridge: 2.5 drams for the infantry down to 2 drams for the shorter weapons.

This rifle, especially those made with a special 5-groove, heavyweight barrel, became the target arm of the Volunteer movements that sprang up in England in the 1850s.

The ·577 Enfield proved its accuracy in the Crimean War. A Rifle Brigade officer silenced a Russian gun crew at a distance of 600m (650yd).

The ·577 Enfield takes its name from the Royal Small Arms factory at Enfield Lock, Middlesex. It was the first mass-produced rifle to be manufactured there.

SHARPS RIFLE

The Sharps carbine of 1851 was one of the first capping breechloaders and utilized a dropping breech block (see page 22 for the principle of this type of ignition). Other main types were the Terry bolt action system and the Westley Richards 'monkey tail' system. Of these the most successful was the Westley Richards, which relied on a tallow-soaked wad at the base of the paper cartridge to seal the breech, held in place by a pivoting arm and plug. The flash from the percussion cap was directed towards the centre of the powder charge, which had the effect of driving the tallow wad against the breech plug to seal the breech, in addition to propelling the bullet down the barrel.

The Sharps carbine relied on the mating of the sloping surface of the breech block with the chamber to effect the seal. This was not very successful and handkerchiefs often had to be tied round the breech to shield the shooter's eyes. Despite this, nearly 100,000 rifles and carbines of this type were used in the American Civil War.

With the introduction of the centre-fire cartridge (see page 24), the famous Sharps buffalo rifles emerged. These were normally made to special order, there being a variety of combinations of calibres, barrel lengths and weights. In 1874 the Winchester, although a repeater, was restricted to comparatively low power loads, the ·50-95, for example, firing a 300 grain lead bullet at 475m/s (1560 ft per sec). The strong action of the Sharps allowed it to take chamberings such as the ·50-140, a 473 grain bullet which could reach a velocity of 480m/s (1580ft per sec).

Sharps also made some of America's first long-range target rifles, the most famous of which was the Borchardt Sharps of 1878 which featured a concealed hammer and long-range sights.

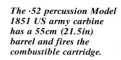

The ·52 percussion Model 1851 US army carbine has a 55cm (21.5in) barrel and fires the combustible cartridge.

The Dreyse 'needle gun', developed by Johann Dreyse in 1829, was the first breechloader adopted for all military purposes, when it was taken up by Prussia in 1848.

The success of this rifle prompted the British government to set up a committee to look for a breechloader, preferably one that could utilize the ·577 Enfield. Jacob Snider, an American, submitted a system that converted the Enfield by removing the percussion breech end and screwing in a breech section with a laterally pivoting breech block that carried a firing pin or striker. The original hammer was retained to hit the striker in place of the original percussion cap and nipple. The breech block was opened by pressing a thumb catch on the left hand side on the MKII and MKIII, the earlier MKI having only a spring-loaded ball holding the block in position. The force of the cartridge was directed backwards and with the heavy hammer driven down on to the striker there was little chance of the block opening on firing. Extraction of the rimmed cartridge case was by means of a claw extractor attached to the block. After opening it was pulled rearwards. The case was not thrown out, as with modern guns, instead the rifle had to be turned over to allow the extracted case to fall out.

The MKI and MKII rifles were conversions of the iron-barrelled Enfields. The MKIII, however, utilized a steel barrel, a first for the British army.

The rifle fired a 480 grain bullet with a muzzle velocity of 380m/s (1250 ft persec). By way of comparison, the modern military rifle fires a 55 grain bullet at about 945m/s (3100 ft per sec).

The original Snider cartridges were made of stiff paper with a metal base, which was inclined to separate from the rest of the case. Colonel Boxer came up with a modification in which coiled brass replaced the paper and breech-sealing without separation of the case head was achieved.

The ·577 Snider breechloader shown is the standard infantry rifle converted from its predecessor, the ·577 Enfield muzzle loader. The later versions, with new barrels, could still use the original Enfield lock and stock.

DERRINGER

There have been small short-barrelled pistols since the flintlock era: these were pocket pistols. Longer ones that could be carried in an overcoat pocket were generally known as travelling pistols and the largest, for carrying in a holster, were known as holster pistols.

The derringer was a pocket pistol that took its name from Henry Derringer, a gunsmith from Philadelphia, who specialized in short-barrelled percussion single-shot pistols of between ·33 and ·50 calibre. They were usually sold in pairs and were introduced in the 1830s. Easily concealed, the little firearm could be carried about the person without anyone having knowledge of its presence – in 1865 John Wilkes Booth walked into the presidential box at Ford's Theater carrying a derringer and shot Abraham Lincoln.

With the coming of the rim-fire cartridge, several gunmakers in America produced these small, generally multi-barrelled pistols. Sharps produced his four-barrelled pistol initially in ·22 and ·30 rim-fire, then later in ·32. Colt produced a single-shot derringer in both ·22 and ·41 rim-fire, but by far the most popular was the

Remington over and under in ·41 rim-fire. The cartridges were not powerful (see page 22) and a well-filled wallet or book in the breast pocket could stop the bullet, which was travelling at some 120m/s (400 ft persec). In recent years Italian firms have produced stronger reproductions of these little pistols for modern cartridges, up to and including the ·44 Magnum.

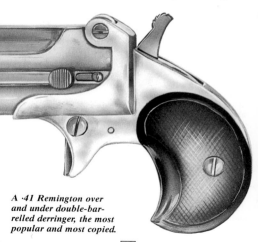

A ·41 Remington over and under double-barrelled derringer, the most popular and most copied.

WINCHESTER 73

Oliver F. Winchester was a successful shirt manufacturer who invested in the Volcanic Arms Co., which made lever action repeating weapons firing a very low-powered cartridge. When this company was forced into receivership Winchester formed the New Haven Arms Co. and continued to produce rifles and carbines like the Volcanic. B. Tyler Henry, Superintendent at Volcanic at this time, realizing the shortcomings of the Volcanic cartridge, developed a ·44 rim-fire cartridge firing a 216 grain bullet with 26g (0.75 oz) of powder, a very marked improvement on the Volcanic. By 1862 an improved Henry Rifle was being made for the ·44 rim-fire cartridge and, in 1866, the name of The Henry Repeating Rifle Co. was changed to The Winchester Repeating Arms Co. After various

The 'gun that won the West', the 73 was Winchester's first rifle to fire the comparatively potent ·44/40 cartridge.

improvements the first rifle with Winchester's name, the Model 66 or ·44 rim-fire, appeared..

The need for more powerful cartridges produced the centre-fire case and with this in ·44/40 (40 grains black powder) the Model 73 was created. As with previous lever action repeaters the magazine was a tube housed below the barrel. Operating the lever withdrew the breech block

chamber. There were many models of the 73 rifle carbine: half magazine, heavy barrel, extra long barrel, but the most famous were the 1 in 1000 rifles. These were rifles that shot exceptionally well and were made up with refinements such as set triggers, a device to enable the trigger pull to be 'set' at very light pulls, i.e., grams rather than kilos. Like the Colt single action, the 73 was made in many calibres

'breaking' a toggle joint and lowering the carrier to collect a cartridge. On closing the lever the carrier was raised in line with the breech and the breech block propelled forwards, carrying the cartridge into the

that would enable both pistol and rifle to shoot the same cartridge.

Manufacture of the Winchester 73 continued until 1919, with over 720,000 rifles being produced.

Colt 45 SA

Known as the Single Action Army, the Peacemaker and the Frontier, this was the most popular handgun in America during the last quarter of the 19th century.

Samuel Colt had been very successful with his percussion revolvers prior to and during the American Civil War, but Rollin White/Smith & Wesson held a patent for a cylinder bored through to the rear for breechloading. This patent expired in 1869 and Colt produced breechloading conversions for his percussion revolvers. These were followed by several rimfire pocket revolvers then,

The Army 19cm (7.5 in) barrel version, showing the side rod ejector housing and the loading gate.

in 1873, the ·45 SA Army appeared. SA (single action) means the hammer must be thumb cocked each time. Double action revolvers can be fired by pulling the trigger, which cocks and releases the hammer and turns and locks the cylinder. The ·45 SA has kept virtually the same design, other than changes in calibre.

1955. The gun can still be purchased today but only in its original calibres. The main variations were in barrel length. The barrel of the Army (Cavalry) model was 19cm (7.5 in), the Artillery 14cm (5.5 in) and the Civilian 12cm (4.75 in). All had a side rod ejector to eject fired cases. The basic models

It was chambered initially for the ·45 Colt cartridge, in 1878 for the Winchester ·44/40, and later for most American centre-fire cartridges, four rim-fire cartridges and the British ·450/·455 range.

Production continued to 1941 then, due to popular demand, recommenced in

had no proper sights but, using the notch milled out in the rear of the frame for the backsight, a good shot could hit a man-sized target at 100m (110 yd). To compete with the target market the Colt SA was produced with target sights and the Bisley had a modified grip that suited target shooting.

LANCASTER PISTOL

Charles Lancaster was originally a barrel maker who, in 1826, set up his own gunmaking company in London. The firm was principally involved in producing good quality shotguns and rifles and

Henry Thorn, who was an apprentice at Lancaster's, eventually bought the business but retained the name. Thorn developed a single trigger mechanism and produced three- and four-barrelled shotguns.

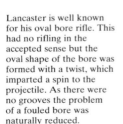

Lancaster is well known for his oval bore rifle. This had no rifling in the accepted sense but the oval shape of the bore was formed with a twist, which imparted a spin to the projectile. As there were no grooves the problem of a fouled bore was naturally reduced.

These, however, did not prove popular.

The English service revolver at this time was considered by some to lack power, due to the leakage that must occur from the gap between the cylinder and the barrel. Army officers firing at charging tribesmen had experienced this power loss. To overcome this, Lancaster produced two- and four-barrelled pistols, usually with his oval bore rifling. These were like ·455/·476 mini shotguns, breaking at the breech for loading. They were all double action and some had a spur to the trigger whereby the mechanism could be brought to full cock with the middle finger and then fired with the trigger finger. Beautifully made, they were a sought after alternative to the revolver.

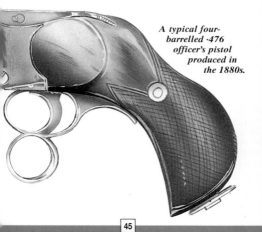

A typical four-barrelled ·476 officer's pistol produced in the 1880s.

BORCHARDT

The Borchardt was the first self-loading pistol to be commercially produced and the first to use a magazine housing in the butt. The design of the breech locking was based on a toggle that formed the design of the famous Luger. The pistol fires an 85 grain, 7.65 mm bullet from a bottle-necked cartridge at a muzzle velocity of 390m/s (1280 ft per sec).

The pistol works on the recoil of the cartridge,

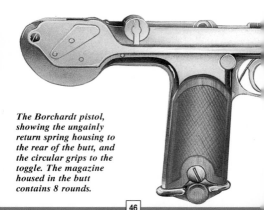

The Borchardt pistol, showing the ungainly return spring housing to the rear of the butt, and the circular grips to the toggle. The magazine housed in the butt contains 8 rounds.

which moves the frame and toggle breech block to the rear. The toggle remains locked for the first few millimetres then, when the pressure has dropped, it breaks, ejecting the fired case and feeding a new one from the magazine. The gun is somewhat ungainly in shape, by virtue of the return spring, which is

patented his own pistol which used Borchardt's principle of breech operation, and eventually manufacture of the Borchardt ceased.

A major failing of the pistol was the difficulty in stripping and reassembling it, a very important consideration with a military weapon.

coiled and housed in the large projection behind the toggle.

The designer, Hugo Borchardt, was employed by Ludwig Löwe of Berlin, who produced the pistol in 1896. However, Georg Luger, who was also employed by the firm,

The Borchardt was supplied with a shoulder stock which converted it into a carbine, a useful feature that followed with the later German military pistols. All pistols manufactured after January 1897 carry the initials DWM on top of the oversize toggle.

LEE ENFIELD RIFLE

Without a doubt the Lee Enfield was the best bolt action military rifle ever produced. The early models, with the Metford barrels, were used across the globe during the last decade of the 19th century and, in various forms, it was the British service rifle for World War I and World War II.

The rifle combined the Lee action initially with a Metford and later the Enfield barrel. James Lee, an American Scot, patented his bolt action rifle with a removable magazine in 1879. In 1888 Britain adopted the Lee system and issued the ·303 Lee Metford MKI with an 8-round magazine firing a 215 grain bullet with a muzzle velocity of 564m/s (1850 ft per sec). The propellant was still black powder. In 1892, the MKII appeared, with a 10-round magazine and firing the cordite load, giving a velocity of 600m/s (1970ft per sec). The Enfield rifled version came out in 1895, shortly followed by a handy carbine.

In 1902, the SMLE with its charge guide was adopted. Known as the Rifle No. 1 SMLE, it underwent minor changes – various long-range sights were fitted and a cut-off to allow single-shot loading, keeping the rounds in the magazine as reserve. Around 1914 the MKVII ·303 cartridge, firing a 174 grain bullet at 743m/s (2440ft per sec), was introduced. The Rifle No. 1 eventually gave way to the No. 4, with its heavier barrel and better sighting. The previous rifle had had a U-notch rearsight and a blade foresight. The No. 4 was fitted with a large-aperture battle sight for up to 180m (200 yd) and an adjustable aperture sight graduated up to 1800m (2000 yd).

The position of the bolt and the ease and smoothness of the action has made this rifle famous for the speed with which it can be fired.

A short magazine Lee Enfield Rifle No. 1 MKIII. It was equipped with a 10-shot detachable box magazine for ·303 calibre cartridges.

MAUSER C96

The German firm of Mauser had been making a military revolver for some years when the Federle brothers, one of whom was superintendent at Mauser, developed a self-loading pistol. In 1894 Paul Mauser became interested in their project and in August 1896 the Kaiser attended a demonstration of this pistol and fired it himself.

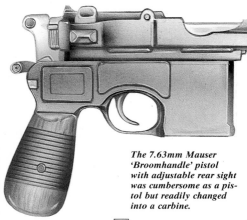

The 7.63mm Mauser 'Broomhandle' pistol with adjustable rear sight was cumbersome as a pistol but readily changed into a carbine.

The pistol is of the locked breech type with a fixed magazine holding ten rounds in front of the trigger guard. It fires a 7.63mm bullet weighing 86 grains with a muzzle velocity of 430m/s (1410 ft per sec) from its 14cm (5.5 in) barrel. The pistol has an external hammer and World War I but recommenced in 1922 and by 1930 a selective fire version was available with a 20-round magazine, giving the user the alternative of fully automatic fire. Winston Churchill, who was with the 21st Lancers, decided to purchase a pistol

very heavy trigger pull, making it difficult to shoot accurately one handed. However, using the rear sight (adjustable from 50 to 1000m/165–3300ft) and once the shoulder stock/holster was fitted, the Mauser became a very useful pistol/carbine. It was used extensively during World War I and a 9mm Parabellum version was produced. Production ceased at the end of rather than use a sword. He selected the Mauser and at the Battle of Omdurman in the Sudan he used it very effectively against the Dervishes.

A longer-barrelled version with a fixed stock was produced, but by 1939 the Mauser factory was too busy making other military pistols and production of the C96 ceased.

MAUSER RIFLE

The Mauser 98 was the principal infantry rifle used by Germany in World War I and, as the modified K98, the principal rifle of World War II. In addition, the action has been used by the majority of manu- facturers for sporting rifles. The action is simple, strong and safe.

The Mauser brothers designed and produced their 1871 Model Service rifle in 11mm calibre, which was a single-shot turn-bolt action. This was then converted to a repeater by using a tubular magazine. The military wanted a clip- loading rifle and in 1898 the famous G98 was adopted by the German army. The turn-bolt design used forward-locking lugs bearing on the base of the cartridges, a box magazine for five rounds and a charge guide for holding a charger or clip of five rounds. Having opened the bolt a charger is inserted in the guide and

the five rounds pushed down into the magazine. The bolt is then operated to feed and extract each cartridge.

The cartridge fires a round-nosed bullet of 226 grains at about 600m/s (2000 ft per sec). Later the bore diameter was increased slightly (from ·318 to ·323) to take the new 8 x 5JS cartridges. This lighter bullet was propelled at 850m/s (2880 ft per sec). – an extremely accurate rifle and cartridge. Germany select-ed the 8 x 57 cartridge Mauser rifle, while other countries, such as Brazil and Spain, used the 7 x 57mm Mauser which fired a lighter 154 grain bullet at around 880m/s (2900ft per sec).

Accuracy tests on a Brazilian Mauser firing the 7mm cartridge carried out at Bisley in 1914 gave a dispersion of 90cm (36in) at 1000m (1100yd), reducing to only 63cm (25in) at 900m (975yd), excellent results for a standard military rifle.

Although not capable of fast-bolt operation, the Mauser rifle G98, shown above, is still the strongest and safest of all military rifles. No other action has been so widely used and so often copied for military and sporting rifles.

LUGER

No other single pistol can be found with as many variations as the Luger and, next to the Colt Single Action, it probably stands as the pistol most sought after by collectors.

Georg Luger used Hugo Borchardt's basic design (see page 26) and, following various prototypes, the 1900 model came into production. This was a 7.65mm calibre pistol with a 11cm (4.75 in) barrel and was immediately adopted by the Swiss army. Two years later a carbine version was produced with a 30cm (11.75 in) barrel. In 1904 Luger experimented with the 7.65mm bottle-neck cartridge, opening it out to take a 9mm bullet, and the 1904 Naval Model was born. This pistol had a 15cm (6 in) barrel, a two-position rear sight and was adapted for use with a shoulder stock. Other modifications brought

the 1906 model in both 9mm and 7.65mm. In 1908 the Germany army adopted the P08 with its 10cm (4 in) barrel and the 15cm (6 in) Naval model with the 100 and 200m rear sight, both in 9mm.

The majority of those pistols were made at DWM at Karlsruhe and at Erfurt. A pistol for the artillery with a 20cm (8 in) barrel and shoulder stock was produced with a 32-

round 'snail' magazine. There were, of course, other government contract issues for countries such as Portugal, Holland, Turkey and Bulgaria, and in the early days an attempt was made to interest the USA in a ·45 version. The 7.65 version fired a 93 grain bullet at 370m/s (1200 ft per sec) and the 9mm a 125 grain bullet at about 335m/s (1100 ft per sec).

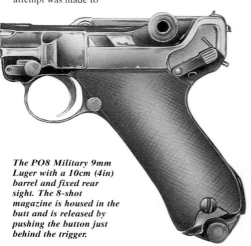

The PO8 Military 9mm Luger with a 10cm (4in) barrel and fixed rear sight. The 8-shot magazine is housed in the butt and is released by pushing the button just behind the trigger.

COLT 1911

This famous ·45 self-loading pistol was the US army firearm from 1912 until just a few years ago. The Colt, like so many other semi- and fully auto-

The ·45ACP 1911 (illustrated) and the later 1911A1 are without doubt the most successful and copied self-loading combat pistols ever made.

matic weapons, was designed by John M Browning and evolved from the Model 1900, the model 1902 and the ·45 model 1905.

All these models, and the 1911, worked on the locked breech recoil system: on firing the barrel and breech are locked together via mating lugs and grooves. Both barrel and breech move back about 47mm (0.2in) then, as the barrel is attached to the frame by means of a link, it is pulled down out of engagement, allowing the breech to travel fully backwards ejecting and

feeding a cartridge from the magazine loaded into the butt and cocking the hammer.

Colt worked hard to get his pistols approved by the US government, who insisted on ·45 calibre, and he succeeded. Around 500,000 1911 pistols were made between 1912 and 1918 for the army; additionally there were the better finished commercial ones. Owing to demand the pistol was made by Springfield Armory, Remington and others. It was also made in Norway between 1917 and the early 1930s and issued to the RAF in ·455 Webley Automatic calibre. In 1926 the 1911 AI with several improvements was adopted. Some two and a half million had been produced by the end of World War II.

WEBLEY & SCOTT MKVI

The Webley MKVI was the last of a line of ·455 calibre hinged frame revolvers that were the issue side arms to the British Services, starting with the MKI in 1887 to the MKVI introduced in 1915. They were of the simultaneous extraction type, which means that on opening the pistol the extractor is activated, ejecting all cartridges, fired or not.

The hinged frame revolver can be traced back to 1868 by virtue of patents taken out by Tranter. Other patents, by Pryse and Kaufmann, were taken out for similar systems and in 1883 the stirrup latch for holding the action closed came into being. Around this time Webley and Green teamed up and produced the excellent Webley WG series of revolvers, making target versions until 1902.

They were made in a 15cm (6in) Army version and also with a 19cm (7.5in) barrel and adjustable sight for target shooting. The WGs were all black powder weapons with Metford rifling and calibres of ·450 ·455 and ·476. The ·476 was basically a ·455 with a bullet that measured ·476 at its maximum diameter. The British government models made by Webley & Scott were the MKI to

MKVI. Barrel length for military use changed from 10cm (4 in) to 15cm (6 in) and the shape of the grip changed. Other modifications to the cylinder release were carried out, but otherwise the pistol was the same with exception of proofing for the cordite load.

The 10cm (4 in) MKV started off in World War I but was superseded by the MKVI in 1915. The ·455 bullet weighed 265 grains and was propelled with a muzzle velocity varying between 180 and 230m/s (600–750 ft per-sec) depending on the propellant.

The Webley & Scott MKVI ·455 6-shot self-extracting service revolver proved strong and reliable in combat.

WALTHER PPK

The PPK, immortalized in the James Bond films, has the ability to fire the first round double action, i.e. it can be carried safely with a cartridge in the chamber

The PPK (Polizei Pistole Kriminale) is a compact and accurate self-loading pocket pistol with safety features that were way ahead of its time.

and the hammer at rest. Carl Walther produced his first pistol in 1906. This was a semi-automatic, 6.35mm pocket pistol. From 1909 to 1921 Models 2 to 9 were produced, all traditional blow-back operated semi-autos in 6.35, 7.65 and 9mm short calibres. Although the Model 9 remained in production until 1945 the advent of the Model PP (Police Pistol) in 1929 put all other pocket or small holster pistols very much in the shade. This was the first successful double-action self-loading pistol and was shortly followed by the shorter-barrelled PPK. Barrel length of the PP was 8.5cm (3.35 in) with an overall length of 16.2cm (6.38 in), while the PPK was 1cm (1/2 in) shorter. The PP was designed to be carried in a holster by uniformed police and the PPK in the pocket by plainclothes police. Both were highly successful and the PP was adopted by the German services; manufacture continued throughout World War II. Both pistols were available in three calibres: ·22 LR, 7.6 mm and 9mm short (the 9mm Parabellum was too powerful for the blow-back action). The double-action system and safety enabled the pistol to be carried safely with a cartridge in the chamber. A heavy trigger pull was needed to cock the hammer and fire the first round.

The PPK's pocket-size and excellent reputation has made it popular with undercover police.

TOMMY GUN

The tommy gun was the first sub-machine-gun to be used by the US army, which purchased it in 1928 (although it was produced from 1919). It is a ·45 calibre gun with either a 20-round box or a 50-round drum magazine.

John T. Thompson was a retired brigadier-general and his life-long ambition had been to produce an automatic rifle. A US naval commander, John

Blish, patented a delayed blow-back system for automatic weapons in 1915 and he and Thompson founded the Auto-Ordnance Co.. Although Blish's system, which worked on the principle of a sloping wedge locking the breech block (unlocking when chamber pressure dropped), did not suit the high-pressure rifle cartridge – it did work with the ·45 Automatic Colt Pistol cartridge – and the American sub-machine-gun was born. Colt and Savage Arms Corp. made the guns for the British in World War II but there were two main disadvantages: the weight, over 4.5kg (10 lb), and the production cost. These two factors brought about its demise and the M3, the 'grease gun', was adopted. The Thompson fired the 230 grain ·45 calibre bullet at just under 275m/s (900 ft per sec). The velocity may not compare with a rifle but the heavy bullet gave the knockdown power required for this short-range weapon.

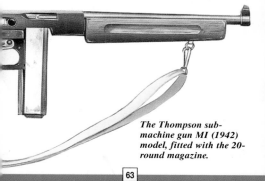

The Thompson sub-machine gun MI (1942) model, fitted with the 20-round magazine.

MG34

Designed by Mauser, the MG34 was an outstanding general purpose machine-gun with virtually all the attributes necessary to lead the way in future machine-gun design. It had a high rate of fire (800–900 rounds/min), easy barrel changing simple field stripping and could fire either belt or 50- and 75-round drum magazines. It weighed 19kg (42lb) and was capable of automatic or semi-automatic fire. There was no change-over lever to select fire – pulling the

The MG34 general purpose machine gun, showing the perforated barrel cover to assist air cooling, and its folding bi-pod. The drum magazine is not shown.

trigger at the top gave semi-auto mode and at the bottom full auto.

The gun works on the locked recoil system, utilizing the gas pressure behind the bullet expanding in a muzzle attachment to assist with the rearwards movement of the barrel. It is locked by the rotating bolt head.

Although the MG34 was good, the MG42 was bet-ter. The rate of fire was increased to 1200 rounds /min and the weapon was only fully automatic. A quicker method of barrel changing was devised, brought about by the exceptionally high rate of fire – the fastest firing machine-gun in World War II. This gun was very similar to the MG34 but did not utilize the rotating bolt system for locking; instead locking lugs are forced into slots at the moment of firing. Both machine-guns fired the standard military rifle car-tridge, the 8 x 57JS, and were air cooled.

BREN GUN

The ·303 Bren light machine-gun was developed from the Czech ZB26 produced at Brno and the Enfield Royal Small Arms Factory, its name is a combination of the two producers. It was to replace the Lewis machine-gun as a platoon weapon for general infantry and production started at Enfield in 1937. It was later also produced by Inglis in Canada.

There were four models, the first two weighing about 10kg (22 lb) with a 63cm (25 in) barrel and capable of using either the 30-round box magazine or 100-round drum magazine. The later versions had slightly shorter barrels, were some 15 per cent lighter and only took the 30-round magazine.

The gun was usually fired from a prone position, using the attached bipod, which could be folded up for carrying. In addition it could be attached to a fixed line tripod or an anti-aircraft tripod and was carried on a gun carrier in World War II. Fired from the hip with the aid of a sling the gun was very efficient for street fighting. The rear sight was an aperture and the foresight a blade, both set off to the left as the magazine sat centrally over the open breech.

The gun was capable of fully automatic or single-shot semi-automatic fire. On full automatic it was capable of very controlled three-shot bursts. The Bren was gas operated – part of the gases caused by the cartridge exploding would push back the piston and breech block with its locking mechanism, which was returned by a spring housed in the butt.

The Bren ·303 light machine-gun MKI, showing the 30-round magazine in place and fitted with the standard bipod. As the magazine is centred, the sights are offset to the left.

In 1920 John C. Garand produced a semi-auto-matic rifle, based on the primer being blown back about 1mm (0.03in). This meant that on firing there was a tremendous build-up of pressure in the cartridge. As the bullet began its path down the barrel, the brass cartridge case would expand and the primer move towards the rear where it would be restrained by the bolt and striker. This movement against the striker caused the action to unlock. The system was not adopted but the US government employed Garand at Springfield Armory to come up with a suitable self-loading rifle for the .30/06 cartridge. This he did and in 1937 production of the M1 rifle commenced, ending only in 1945. Over four million of Garand's rifles were produced in this period.

The rifle was a charger-loaded, 8 shot, gas operat-ed type, notable because of the short receiver. This was achieved by housing the bolt return spring inside the operating lug which acted as the gas piston. Gas from the fired cartridge escaped through a port about 4cm (1.5 in) from the muzzle and thrust the operating rod backwards, working the bolt. The bolt was of the rotating type, activated by the cam surface of the operating lug. When the last round had been fired the charge was automatically ejected and the action stayed open to receive a new charger.

The rifle proved to be extremely reliable during World War II and accelerated the US government's aim to adopt a selective fire weapon, achieved with the 7.62 Nato M14.

Sniper versions of the M1 were produced, as well as a National Match model with special barrel and sight. The M1 fired the ·30/06 cartridge, a 150 grain bullet, at a velocity of 822m/s (2700 ft per sec).

America's first self-loading military rifle, the ·30/06 US rifle M1 with non-detachable 8-shot clip-loaded magazine.

SNIPER'S RIFLE

A Colonial backwoodsman, armed with his Kentucky or Pennsylvania rifle, could hit an English Redcoat officer quite easily at 200m (216 yd), but real sniping had to wait for the production of an accurate long-range rifle. This was feasible as long ago as the 1860s and during the American Civil War the Whitworth ·451 muzzle-loading rifle fitted with a tube sight was used by both sides. Concealment, to avoid counter-sniper fire, was also very important, but this was difficult in the days of black powder because of the smoke that issued from the discharged weapon. In some cases light artillery would be used to knock out the sniper.

The 7 x 57 Mauser with its ordinary open sight was used by the Boers for sniping and during World War I both sides carried out extensive sniping. The

The rifle illustrated is the ·303 Lee Enfield No. 4 MK1 (T), adopted for sniper use in 1942 and fitted with a No. 32 telescopic sight and wooden cheek rest.

British rifle was either the SMLE or, preferably, the P14, which was an American-made rifle based on a modified Mauser action and fitted with a low-powered Aldis telescopic sight. The Germans, of course, used their Mauser G98 fitted with a variety of telescopic sights (see page 52).

Sniping continued into World War II and a specially barrelled Lee Enfield No. 4 was made up with a raised cheek piece to align the marksman's eye with the low-powered telescopic sight.

The American sniper's rifle was either an accurate heavy-barrelled Winchester or a Remington rifle fitted with a variable scope up to x16 power, capable of putting every shot into 1cm (0.5 in) at 200m (216 yd). The record for the longest sniping shot, however – 2363m (2600 yd) – dates from the war in Vietnam and was carried out with a scope-sighted ·50 heavy machine-gun!

COLT PYTHON

This revolver is the finest of the Colt range. In 1930 Colt's main competitors, Smith & Wesson, brought the ·357 cartridge. Colt brought out their New Service and Single Action in ·357. In 1954 Colt

out their 38/44 Outdoorsman, a large-framed revolver which took the ·38 Special cartridge, bullet diameter being .357. By 1935 the cartridge case was lengthened by about 0.25cm (0.1 in) so that it would not chamber in a ·38 Special. In 1935, using different powder, the ·357 Magnum was created.

Smith & Wesson led the way with new models for

brought out their ·357 Magnum to replace the New Service and then, a year later, the Python appeared. It was, and still is, a beautifully finished revolver and the first to have the distinctive full length ejector shroud. It also has a ventilated top rib to the barrel – a first again. The lockwork is hand finished, making it the smoothest operating double-action revolver to come straight out of the factory box. The pistol is a little heavy, being 1.2kg (44oz) with a 15cm (6 in) barrel but this is an advantage when shooting .357 Magnum loads. It will also fire the ·38 Special cartridge. Barrel lengths vary between 6cm (2.5 in) and 20cm (8 in). The grips were originally chequered walnut but now rubber grips are available. The ·357 cartridge fires a 158 grain bullet at 435m/s (1430 ft per sec), compared with 260m/s (855 ft per sec) for the ·38 Special.

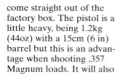

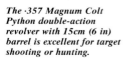

The ·357 Magnum Colt Python double-action revolver with 15cm (6 in) barrel is excellent for target shooting or hunting.

BIG GAME RIFLE

With the growth of the British Empire during the 19th century there was greater opportunity for travellers or military officers serving abroad to hunt African and Indian game. The large and dangerous species hunted on both continents required large calibre rifles (and smoothbore guns) firing heavy bullets – anything less would not provide sufficient knockdown power.

Early rifles used for big game were 10, 8, 4 and even 2 bores, i.e. they fired a ball weighing from about 40g to 240g (1.5oz to 0.5 lb)! They were usually single-barrel percussion rifles heavy enough to make it possible for them to be fired from the shoulder.

With the coming of breech loading very little changed until the advent of smokeless powder and the ability

A typical English double-barrelled sidelock big game rifle, calibres ranging from ·300 Magnum to ·700 Magnum.

to drive a smaller, more conical bullet at greater velocities, giving better penetration and energy. This was then perfected with the classic double rifle with barrels regulated to ensure that, with the given cartridge performance, both barrels would put their shots within 8–10cm (3–4in) at 60–70m (65-76 yd). For those not able to afford the double barrel, single-barrel falling block rifles were made in the big game cartridges and special bolt-action rifles were also developed.

There were many proprietary cartridges and, for example, the Holland and Holland ·375 Magnum developed two-and-a-half times the stopping power of the legal requirement for a deer rifle, while the ·600 nitro express had over four times the power. Armed with a nitro express double rifle the hunter/game warden facing dangerous or wounded animals had the safeguard of being able to fire two shots as quickly as he could squeeze the triggers.

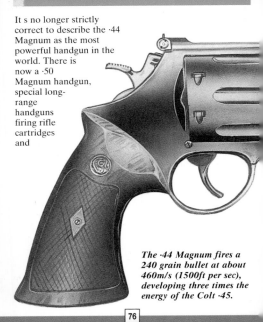

SMITH & WESSON ·44 MAGNUM

It s no longer strictly correct to describe the ·44 Magnum as the most powerful handgun in the world. There is now a ·50 Magnum handgun, special long-range handguns firing rifle cartridges and

The ·44 Magnum fires a 240 grain bullet at about 460m/s (1500ft per sec), developing three times the energy of the Colt ·45.

other custom made combinations. However, the ·44 Magnum remains the most powerful handgun cartridge generally avalable.

accurate cartridge firing a 246 grain bullet at up to 300m/s (1000 ft per sec)

There have been ·44 calibre revolvers since the percussion period. These were converted to fire the ·44 rim-fire cartridge and then revolvers were produced in the ·44 Smith & Wesson American cartridge and in 1870 in the Smith & Wesson Russian cartridge, using, of course, black powder.

In 1907 the longer ·44 Smith & Wesson Special made its debut – a very

with smokeless powder. But why not lengthen the case, strengthen the frame and thicken the chamber walls, to produce higher velocities with different powders? In 1955–56, the result of a joint development between Smith & Wesson and Remington achieved all this. The S&W ·44 Magnum with a 15cm (6 in) barrel produced muzzle energy almost twice that of the ·357 Magnum: a really accurate long-range hunting cartridge had at last been conceived.

ARMALITE RIFLE

The US Operations Research Office (ORO) was set up in 1948 to analyse the effect of small arms fire on casualty reports from both world wars. They came to the conclusion that marksmanship was secondary to volume of fire. The ORO also proved that, while infantry fire had been effective in World War I, battles at up to 1200m (1300 yd) and perhaps 300m (325 yd) in World War II, most hits had been made around 100m (110 yd). A new lightweight assault rifle, capable of full or automatic fire, was required.

Armalite had been established in 1954 to come up with a design for a military rifle made, as far as possible, of plastic and non-ferrous metals. Eugene M. Stoner, famous for previous work on

The ·223 M16 rifle shown here proved an excellent jungle warfare weapon. It was issued to all US troops in Vietnam.

military rifles, produced the AR15, known in military terms as the M16 and M16AT. The rifle is operated by gas from the explosion of the cartridge being taken off from a port towards the muzzle; this gas pressure drives the bolt carrier rearwards. Via a cam arrangement the bolt is rotated to unlock, eject and feed a new cartridge using the force of the action spring. One of the main features of the M16 is the relation-ship of the stock to the barrel:. They are in line, which provides for better manageability on fully automatic fire. Colt Fire-arms acquired the rights to produce the AR15 in 1959 but there was opposition to it firing a small bullet. In 1962 1000 AR15s were ordered to be tested in Vietnam. They were ideally suited to jun-gle warfare. The rifle is ·223 calibre, cartridge des-ignation 5.56 x 45mm (case length), firing a 55 grain bullet at 975m/s (3200 ft per sec), three times the speed of sound.

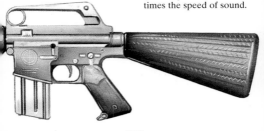

GERMAN HUNTING RIFLE

In and around the deep forests of Germany, Austria and Eastern Europe the hunters' quarry may be deer, boar, rabbit and other small ground game, or winged game such as pheasant or pigeon. To cope with this variety the hunter requires a very versatile weapon, one capable not only of firing a single projectile with sufficient energy to kill a 200kg (450l b) wild boar, but also able to take shot cartridge for use on flying game.

The type of gun illustrated caters for the above needs and is called a 'Drilling' –three barrels. Usually there is a 7 to 9.3mm rifle barrel below a pair of smoothbore shotgun barrels. When the rifle barrel is selected, via the sliding switch, a rear sight regulated for 100m (110 yd) automatically flips up and the front trigger operates

the rifle barrel. This trigger can also be 'set': i.e. by pushing it forwards it will then become a hair trigger. Most Drillings and the more simple over/under rifle/shotguns are fitted with telescopic sights on quickly detachable claw mounts.

With this type of gun the hunter has instant choice between big game and flying birds. In addition, when on a specific wild boar drive the hunter may use solid slug cartridges in both the shotgun barrels. This gives good accuracy and performance on an animal such as wild boar up to about 50m (55 yd).

A good choice of telescopic sight would be a 1.5–6 power x 42mm object lens diameter. This provides low power for fast shots at running boar, combined with suitable power for dusk shooting.

A very versatile combination gun, with a double-barrelled shotgun, a rifle barrel below and a telescopic sight.

UZI

This sub-machine-gun was designed in Israel by Uziel Gal in 1951 and is generally thought to be the best sub-machine-gun yet designed.

Unlike most sub-machine-guns, which rely on a 'safety' notch to engage the cocking piece when carrying the gun loaded, the Uzi has a grip safety, which locks the mechanism, preventing the breech block from moving if the gun is dropped. Field stripping is very simple and the barrel can be readily changed.

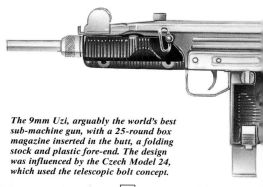

The 9mm Uzi, arguably the world's best sub-machine gun, with a 25-round box magazine inserted in the butt, a folding stock and plastic fore-end. The design was influenced by the Czech Model 24, which used the telescopic bolt concept.

Although first manufactred for use by the Israeli defence forces, the Uzi is now also produced under licence by Fabrique National in Belgium, Germany and several countries in South America. It is used by many police forces and is the favourite weapon of the US Presidential Protection Team.

short barrels. The Uzi has a 25cm (10 in) barrel and overall length, with stock retracted, of 43cm (17 in). This has been accomplished by use of a telescoping bolt that also acts as a secondary ejection post cover, reducing the chance of dust entering the mechanism. The Uzi takes magazines of 25, 32 or 40 rounds and fires the 9mm Parabellum cartridge, 125 grain bullet, at a velocity of 400m/s (1310 ft per sec).

The design of the Uzi stems from the Czech Model 24 sub-machine-gun, which operates on the simple blow-back system suitable for sub-machine-gun cartridges. To keep the overall length down, previous sub-machine-guns had very

STALKING RIFLE

There are perhaps four types of hunting rifles: the heavy big game rifle for large and dangerous animals, the heavy long-range 'varmint' rifle, the lighter double-barrelled rifle, for quick shots at driven game, and the stalking rifle.

The stalking rifle is for the humane control of deer, whether in or around woodland or out on the Scottish hills. It must have great accuracy, be light enough to be carried all day and be capable of firing a bullet of necessary weight and velocity to kill deer-sized animals at ranges of up to 250m (270yd). Woodland stalking is most often carried out in early morning and at last light, so a telescopic sight is an absolute necessity for shooting in poor light. The bolt-action magazine rifle in calibres ranging from the ·243 Winchester to the ·300

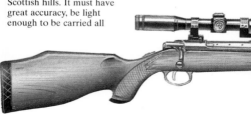

Holland and Holland Magnum and fitted with a good quality 6 x 42mm or variable power telescopic sight is ideal.

Stalking rifles are usually of the bolt-action type with a magazine for 3–5 cartridges. A repeating rifle is preferred to a single shot, as it provides a quick second shot if required. Most modern stalking rifles have tappings or grooves to enable scope mounts and telescopic sights to be fitted, and some do not have open sights. Whatever type of scope is fitted, it must be absolutely secure.

The rifle must be capable of placing three shots in 2.5cm (1in) at 100m (110yd) and should have a crisp trigger pull of not more than 1.8kg (4lb). The safety should be positive and quiet in operation. With these features the competent stalker will be able to place a bullet correctly to ensure a humane kill.

The rifle shown is typical of any bolt-action magazine rifle for stalking, fitted with open sights and a telescopic sight.

AK47

Designed by Mikhail T. Kalashnikov in 1947 some 40 million of these assault rifles have been produced worldwide. It has been made in eastern Europe, North Korea and, in modified form, in Finland.

The original gun had a heavy stamped steel receiver (the part containing the bolt, etc. and to which the barrel is fixed),

resulting in an overall weight of 4.3kg (9.5 lb), too heavy for an assault rifle. To get round this, forged/machined receivers were introduced and, in 1959, the modernized AKM, was perfected by reverting to a better stamped steel receiver, achieving a reduced weight of 3.1kg (just under 7lb). The AKMS variation replaced the

The Kalashnikov or AK47 assault rifle, shown with its 30-round magazine in place. This is the later model (AKM) and has the fixed wooden stock. The bolt carrier housing and tap-off point for the gas are seen above the barrel.

fixed wooden stock with a folding steel stock and a small compensator fitted to the muzzle to help keep it down on full automatic.

The gun is capable of semi- or fully automatic fire, and fires from a locked bolt. The breech mechanism operates by gas tapped off from the barrel 15cm (6in) from the muzzle, used to drive back the bolt carrier situated above the barrel. As the bolt carrier moves back the rotating bolt is unlocked via a cam arrangement and returned to close, having picked up a cartridge via the action of the return spring. Sights are relatively simple, being a post foresight and a V rear sight adjustable up to 800m (870yd) on the AK47 and 1000m (1100yd) on the AKM. It fires the 7.62 x 39mm cartridges, giving a muzzle velocity of 710m/s (2330 ft per sec) with a 122 grain bullet and a cyclic rate of fire of 600 rounds/min.

Action: The working parts of the gun to which the barrel is attached.

Bolt: A turning breech-block that resists the rearwards force of the charge and feeds and ejects the cartridge.

Bore: Barrel size based on the number of lead balls to the pound fired by the gun, e.g. a 16-bore gun fires 1-oz balls.

Breech: The end of the barrel that contains the force of the charge.

Breech-block: The opening part of the breech that resists the rearwards force of the charge.

Blow back: A system used in repeating

weapons where the breech is not locked.

Butt: Part of the stock that is held against the shoulder.

Calibre: Internal diameter of the barrel.

Chamber: The part of the breech that accepts the cartridge.

Cock: The part of a gun lock that holds the flint.

Cam: Part of a machine-gun that turns the bolt to lock and unlock the mechanism.

Carbine: A short-barrelled rifle or gun used by cavalry or artillery.

Cylinder: The part of a revolver that holds the cartridges.

Charger: A steel clip holding five to ten cartridges.

Charger guide: A machined slot in the receiver to take the charger.

Cut off: A device enabling single shot loading by stopping cartridges being fed from the magazine.

Double action: Activating the hammer and rotating the cylinder by pulling the trigger.

Falling block: A single shoot action using a vertically sliding breech-block.

Frizzen: Part of the flintlock that is struck by the flint (see also steel).

Firing pin: Part of the action that strikes the primer.

Rim-fire: A cartridge containing detonating powder in its rim.

Set trigger: A device for reducing the trigger pull.

Self-loading: A repeating weapon that uses the energy of the cartridge to enable a shot to be fired each time the trigger is pulled.

Serpentine: The arm holding the slow match in a matchlock.

Slow match: A saltpetre soaked piece of hemp used with a matchlock.

Side rod ejector: The spring-loaded rod attached to the side of the barrel used to eject the fired cases from a revolver.

Single action: The need to thumb cock the hammer to engage the trigger and turn the cylinder.

Stock: The generally wooden part of the gun into which the barrel/action is fitted.

Striker: The part of the action driven into the primer by the hammer.

Steel: The part of the lock that is struck by a flint.

Vent: The small hole at the breech end of a muzzle loading barrel connecting the priming powder to the main charge.